CHARLIE AND THE CHOCOLATE FACTORY

ROALD DAHL

Illustrations by Quentin Blake

Level 3

**Retold by
Caroline Laidlaw**

Series Editors: Annie Hughes and Melanie Williams

Pearson Education Limited
Edinburgh Gate, Harlow,
Essex CM20 2JE, England
and Associated Companies throughout the world.

ISBN 978-0-582-45618-1
This adaptation first published by Penguin Books 2001
Text copyright © Roald Dahl Nominee Ltd, 1964

20

Illustrations copyright © Quentin Blake, 2001
The moral right of the illustrator has been asserted

Design by Wendi Watson
Printed in China
SWTC/20

Published by Pearson Education Ltd in association with
Penguin Books Ltd, a Penguin Random House company.

For a complete list of the titles available in the Penguin Young Readers series
please write to your local Pearson Education office or to:
Penguin Readers Marketing Department, Pearson Education
Edinburgh Gate, Harlow, Essex CM20 2JE

CONTENTS

CHAPTER ONE
The Bucket Family

This is a story about a boy called Charlie Bucket.

There were six people in his family, but none of them were Charlie's brothers or sisters. So who were they?

First, Mr and Mrs Bucket, Charlie's mother and father.

The other four people were Charlie's grandparents. They were so old they stayed in bed all day and never got up. But they didn't have much room because they slept in the SAME bed,

Grandpa Jo and Grandma Josephine at one end,

Grandpa George and Grandma Georgina at the other.

Charlie's House

Charlie's family lived in a very small house. It wasn't easy for them, they were so poor. His mother tried hard to make nice meals. But it was always cabbage, or bread, or potatoes, or more cabbage. Charlie dreamed of eating something else. Most of all, he dreamed of CHOCOLATE!

The Chocolate Factory

In Charlie's town, near his house, there was a chocolate factory. It was the biggest and most famous chocolate factory in the world. All day long, he could smell that most delicious chocolate smell.

'If I had just ONE wish,' Charlie thought, 'I would go inside that factory.'

CHAPTER FOUR

The First Golden Ticket

One day, Grandpa Jo was reading the newspaper.

'Charlie, listen. Five Golden Tickets, each in a bar of Wonka chocolate. Find one, and visit the chocolate factory!'

The next day, Augustus found the first ticket. He was a greedy boy, and nobody liked him.

Here is Augustus with his mother.

CHAPTER FIVE

The Second Golden Ticket

The next lucky child was Veruca. Her parents bought her thousands of Wonka bars. Veruca couldn't wait to open them. She just lay on the floor, kicked her legs and shouted, 'Where's my Golden Ticket! I want my Golden Ticket!'

When at last someone found one, she was happy.

CHAPTER SIX
Charlie's Birthday

Three tickets left! Charlie hoped he would be lucky.
Every year on his birthday, his family gave him a delicious bar of
Wonka chocolate. Perhaps this year it would have a Golden
Ticket inside. How happy Charlie would be!

Did he find a Golden Ticket? What do you think?

The Third Golden Ticket

Poor Charlie! But someone else was much happier. It was Violet, who found the third ticket. This girl loved chewing gum. She always had some in her mouth. If anyone found a piece of gum on their clothes, she just laughed. Grandma Georgina thought she was a horrible child.

The Fourth Golden Ticket

Soon after Charlie's birthday, Grandma Josephine was reading the newspaper.

'Listen, a horrible boy called Mike has found a Golden Ticket!'

Mike was crazy about television. He watched it all the time. If anyone tried to talk to him, he would shout, 'Go away! Can't you see I'm watching television?'

CHAPTER NINE
Charlie Finds Some Money

A few days later, Charlie was walking home from school. It was a very cold day. Suddenly, he saw something in the snow. It was some money. To Charlie this meant only one thing… FOOD.

'I must give it to my mum,' he thought.

'But first, perhaps I'll…'

CHAPTER TEN

A Bar of Chocolate, Please

The kind of food Charlie was thinking about was chocolate. In no time at all, he was inside a shop. After buying a bar of Wonka chocolate he quickly pulled off the paper. What a delicious smell!

Then Charlie saw something yellow under the chocolate. He couldn't believe his eyes.

CHAPTER ELEVEN
The Fifth Golden Ticket

A few minutes later, Charlie arrived back home.
  'I've found it, I've found it!' he shouted.
  'Found what?' asked his grandparents.
  'A Golden Ticket!' answered Charlie.

'Hooray!'
shouted Grandpa Jo,
'Hooray!'

Then, forgetting
where he was, he
jumped high in the air.
His soup went all over
Grandma Josephine!

CHAPTER TWELVE

The Big Day

At last the day arrived. It was a lovely sunny morning. Hundreds of people were standing outside the famous factory. They were waiting to see the children who were going inside for the day.

'Stand back! Stand back!' said a policeman as a line of people walked past.

Veruca came first, wearing an expensive skirt and jacket.
Next came Mike, dressed like someone in a TV film. Then
came Augustus and Violet. All these children had their
parents with them. But not Charlie, who was last in the line.
He had Grandpa Jo.

CHAPTER THIRTEEN

Meet Mr Willy Wonka

Ten o'clock. Time to begin. But where was Mr Willy Wonka?

Then someone shouted, 'That's him!' And so it was! All eyes turned towards the funny little man with his pointed beard.

'My *dear* children,' he said, 'How *do* you do? And *these* are your parents? How *nice*! Come in!'

CHAPTER FOURTEEN
Happy Workers

What an amazing place! Inside the factory there were beautiful green fields, trees, flowers, and a brown river.

'Look! Near the waterfall!' said Veruca.

'Lots of little dolls! Are they people?'

'Why, yes they are,' said Mr Wonka. 'They're Oompa-Loompas. Famous for working, dancing and singing.'

CHAPTER FIFTEEN

Augustus Falls in the River

While the Oompa-Loompas sang, Augustus walked down to the river.

'It must be full of chocolate,' he thought. He lay on his stomach to taste it. Delicious!

'Be careful! You'll fall in!' shouted Mr Wonka.

SPLASH!

Too late. Augustus was in the river. Then suddenly, he was gone.

CHAPTER SIXTEEN
Down the Chocolate River

'Augustus! Where's Augustus? I'll never see him again!' cried his mother.

'Yes, you *will*,' answered Mr Wonka. 'But not now. What a bad boy!'

It was time to sail down the chocolate river. Charlie looked around. Everything in this amazing world was made of sugar. The pink boat was sugar!

CHAPTER SEVENTEEN

The Magic Room

The Oompa-Loompas rowed the boat down a long tunnel. They stopped opposite a door in the wall.

'This is the most important room in the factory,' said Mr Wonka. 'Come inside!'

What a place! Magic sweets of every kind! Like green Gobstoppers that never got any smaller in your mouth.

CHAPTER EIGHTEEN

The Great Gum Machine

In the middle of the room was a great big metal machine. It moved up and down, making a very loud noise.

CLONK, CLATTER, BANG!

Suddenly, out came something small, and flat.

'It's chewing gum!' Violet shouted.

'That's right,' said Mr Wonka. 'The most amazing gum in the world!'

CHAPTER NINETEEN

Goodbye, Violet

'It's magic gum, you see,' said Mr Wonka. 'This piece tastes of soup, meat, and blueberry pie.'

Violet put the gum in her mouth. Mmm! Delicious!

'Help!' cried her mother. 'She's turning purple and…'

'…Round,' said Mr Wonka. 'Like a blueberry! Oompa-Loompas, take her away! Get the juice out!'

The Nut Room

The next stop was the Nut Room where hundreds of little animals were opening nuts.

'I want a little animal!' shouted Veruca, trying hard to catch one.

But the animals caught *her* and pushed her down with the rubbish. Then down went Veruca's mother.

And what happened to her father?

CHAPTER TWENTY-ONE

The Great Glass Lift

There were only five visitors left now. They were all feeling tired.

'I want to watch television,' said Mike.

'Fine,' said Mr Wonka. 'We'll take the lift.'

The machine was as fast as a rocket. It could go up and down, and round corners. It was crazy!

CHAPTER TWENTY-TWO
The Television Chocolate Room

The visitors stepped out of the lift into a brilliant white room. Then they put on dark glasses.

'This is where we test our Television Chocolate,' said Mr Wonka.

'What do you mean?' asked Mike.

'Well, with a TV camera we send it to another place. It goes by television.'

Mike, is That You?

'It arrives much smaller. Watch this!'

Six Oompa-Loompas put a BIG piece of chocolate under the camera. Suddenly it was in the TV!

Mike went under the camera.

'He's so small,' cried Mike's mum.

'It's all right,' said Mr Wonka. 'The Oompa-Loompas will make him big again.'

Where Next?

Then Mr Wonka turned to Charlie and said, 'My dear boy, you are the only boy left. Well done! You've won! Step into the lift. Here we go!'

Charlie was very surprised. 'What have I won?' he thought. 'Where are we going?'

The Other Children Go Home

The lift flew up into the sky. The people below looked very small.

'Look!' said Mr Wonka, 'The other children! Augustus at the front, Mike at the back. I'm going to give them sweets to take home. But for you, Charlie, something else!'

The lift was right above Charlie's house.

CHAPTER TWENTY-SIX

A Big Surprise

'Charlie,' said Mr Wonka, 'you've won my factory! It's YOURS!'

Charlie couldn't think. The lift was falling.

C R A S H!

'HELP!' cried Grandma Josephine. 'The end of the world!'

But it was just the beginning.

'We're going to live in Charlie's chocolate factory,' said Grandpa Joe. 'We'll never be hungry again!'

ACTIVITIES

1. Look at the book cover.
   What do you think?
   Tick YES, or NO, or I DON'T KNOW.

	YES	NO	I DON'T KNOW
a. Are there any children in this story?			
b. Are there any old people in this story?			
c. Is the story about animals?			
d. Is the story about a boy and a chocolate factory?			
e. Will it be a sad story?			
f. Will it be a magic story?			

AFTER YOU READ

2. The names in Charlie's family tree are wrong.

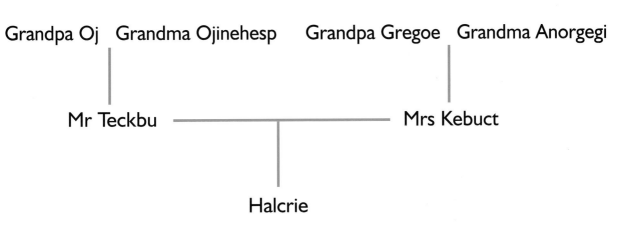

3. True or false?

    a. Mr Willy Wonka's factory made cars.

    b. Six people found Golden Tickets.

    c. Augustus was fat because he ate too much chocolate.

    d. Charlie fell down with the rubbish in the factory.

    e. Mike got smaller and smaller in the TV Chocolate Room.

    f. The magic lift was made of chocolate.

4. Who wrote this story? Complete the puzzle to find out.

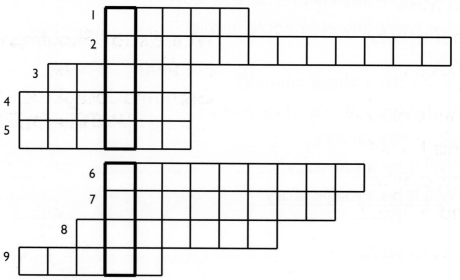

1. You can travel on it in a boat.

2. The happy workers in the factory.

3. The magic lift was made of ....

4. The girl who loved chewing gum.

5. The colour of the tickets.

6. "Chocolate is ....!" says Charlie.

7. The greediest boy in the story.

8. The luckiest boy in the story.

9. Mr Wonka's first name.